Maths
made easy

Key Stage 2
ages 8-9
Workbook 3

Author and Consultant
Sean McArdle

LONDON • NEW YORK • SYDNEY • MOSCOW • DELHI

Adding and subtracting

Add 100 to 356.

456

Add 1 000 to 2 376.

3 376

Subtract 100 from 5 324.

5 224

Subtract 1 000 from 7 296.

6 296

Add 100 to each number.

376	795	646	585
286	57	4 312	5 634
12	4 789	924	3 903

Add 1 000 to each number.

485	607	37	943
3 587	7 056	5 045	2 907
5 897	9 564	5 499	9 001

Subtract 100 from each number.

364	729	477	765
103	146	1 003	599
100	5 745	3 078	6 107

Subtract 1 000 from each number.

4 734	8 610	5 307	9 362
12 675	4 907	8 445	1 001
1 400	15 638	20 832	14 056

Dividing by 10 and 100

Divide 90 by 10.	Divide 3 400 by 100.
9	34

Divide each number by 10.

60	80	10	50
100	150	230	300
210	170	20	260
40	360	590	730
420	380	820	540

Divide each number by 100.

300	700	900	100
600	800	1 100	1 400
1 700	1 900	2 300	2 800
3 800	4 100	8 400	9 400
6 000	1 000	7 500	5 600

Divide each number by 10.

700	2 300	4 100	3 650
6 480	7 080	3 540	2 030
1 030	9 670	6 320	1 400
300	900	1 020	3 660
20	18 000	13 600	17 890

Negative numbers

This is the temperature outside at midnight.

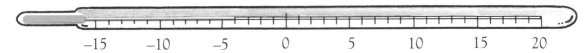

The temperature rises by 12°C by midday. What is the temperature at midday?   *8°C*

The temperature on each of these thermometers rises by 8°C. What is the new temperature each time?

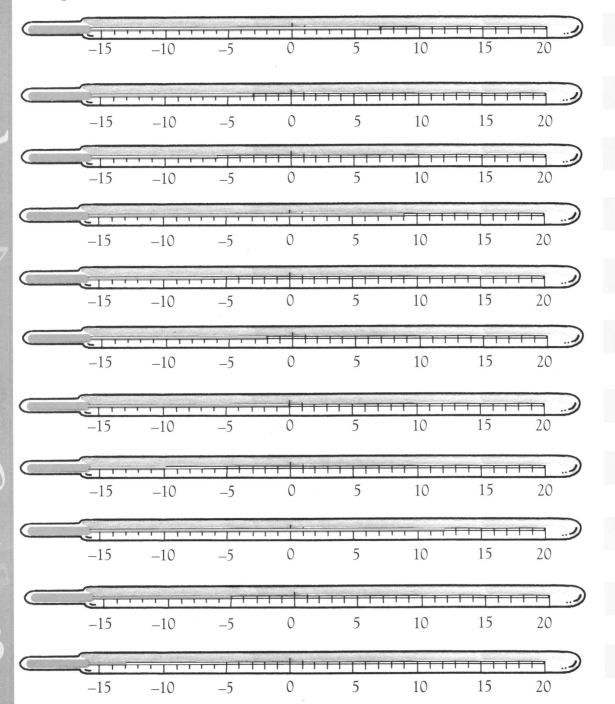

Counting in steps

Continue each sequence.

| 11 | 22 | 33 | 44 | 55 | 66 | 77 | 88 |
| 12 | 24 | 36 | 48 | 60 | 72 | 84 | 96 |

Continue each sequence.

12	23	34	45	56
9	21	33	45	57
32	43	54	65	76
2	14	26	38	50
−20	−9	2	13	24
−30	−18	−6	6	18
−41	−30	−19	−8	3
−60	−48	−36	−24	−12

Continue each sequence.

45	34	23	12	1
70	58	46	34	22
44	33	22	11	0
48	36	24	12	0
7	−4	−15	−26	−37
14	2	−10	−22	−34
8	−3	−14	−25	−36
10	−2	−14	−26	−38

Multiples

Circle the multiples of 11.

9 16 (22) 34 (44) 60 (77) 90

Circle the multiples of 12.

14 26 39 (48) 63 (72) 94 100

Circle the multiples of 11.

1	7	11	18	24	32	44	58
6	13	22	34	44	54	66	77
11	14	21	26	55	88	99	100
20	25	30	35	40	45	50	55
66	26	46	64	44	24	62	72
16	24	32	40	48	56	64	72
11	22	33	44	55	66	78	88
96	73	11	45	62	77	14	33

Circle the multiples of 12.

4	8	12	16	20	24	28	32
9	12	15	18	21	24	27	30
6	12	18	24	30	36	42	48
8	16	24	32	40	48	56	64
9	18	27	36	45	54	63	72
10	20	30	40	50	60	70	80
12	24	36	48	60	72	84	96
68	56	44	32	20	12	0	36

Square numbers

The square has two rows and two columns. It is 2^2.

How many dots are there?   4

2^2 is the same as
$2 \times 2 = 4$

Draw a picture like the one above to show each of these numbers.

3^2

How many
dots are there?

4^2

How many
dots are there?

5^2

How many
dots are there?

6^2

How many
dots are there?

7^2

How many
dots are there?

8^2

How many
dots are there?

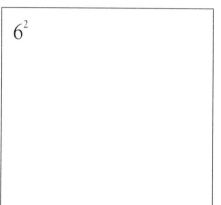

9^2

How many dots are there?

10^2

How many dots are there?

Fractions and decimals

Write each fraction as a decimal.

$\frac{1}{4}$ $\frac{1}{2}$ $\frac{3}{4}$ $\frac{1}{5}$

$\frac{2}{5}$ $\frac{3}{5}$ $\frac{4}{5}$ $\frac{1}{10}$

$\frac{2}{10}$ $\frac{3}{10}$ $\frac{4}{10}$ $\frac{5}{10}$

$\frac{6}{10}$ $\frac{7}{10}$ $\frac{8}{10}$ $\frac{9}{10}$

Write each decimal as a fraction.

0.8   0.5   0.3   0.4

0.25   0.7   0.2   0.75

0.2   0.6   0.5   0.8

0.1   0.4   0.6   .   0.9

Write the answer in the box.

Which two of the fractions above are the same as 0.5?

Which two of the fractions above are the same as 0.8?

Which two of the fractions above are the same as 0.6?

Which two of the fractions above are the same as 0.2?

Which two of the fractions above are the same as 0.4?

Fractions of shapes

Shade $\frac{3}{5}$ of each shape.

 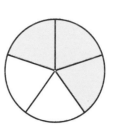

Shade $\frac{4}{5}$ of each shape.

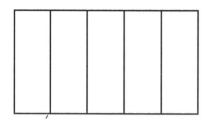

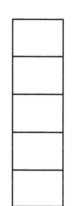

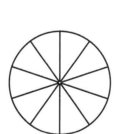

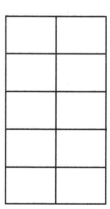

Shade the amount shown of each shape.

Two-fifths

Four-fifths

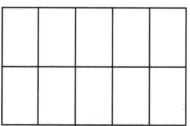

Three-tenths

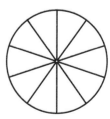

Seven-tenths

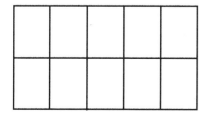

Three-fifths

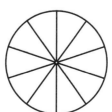

Nine-tenths

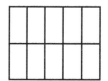

Ordering decimals

Write each row in order starting with the smallest.

| 1.7 m | 1.3 m | 1.5 m | 1.9 m | 1.3 m | 1.5 m | 1.7 m | 1.9 m |
| 5.3 m | 2.8 m | 3.9 m | 1.6 m | 1.6 m | 2.8 m | 3.9 m | 5.3 m |

Write each row in order starting with the smallest.

2.4 m 2.8 m 2.1 m 2.6 m 2.9 m

5.2 m 5.7 m 5.1 m 5.8 m 5.3 m

1.4 m 1.7 m 1.8 m 1.1 m 1.9 m

3.8 m 3.6 m 3.4 m 3.2 m 3.1 m

7.5 m 7.3 m 7.9 m 7.2 m 7.8 m

4.3 m 4.6 m 4.0 m 4.2 m 4.8 m

6.9 m 6.0 m 6.4 m 6.2 m 6.7 m

10.6 m 10.3 m 10.8 m 10.5 m 10.0 m

7.4 m 6.4 m 9.4 m 2.4 m 8.4 m

3.7 m 6.7 m 7.7 m 2.7 m 9.7 m

4.5 m 1.5 m 3.5 m 8.5 m 10.5 m

6.9 m 1.9 m 8.9 m 9.9 m 5.9 m

0.6 m 2.6 m 1.6 m 6.6 m 9.6 m

3.5 m 1.8 m 2.7 m 4.3 m 7.9 m

7.6 m 2.3 m 4.9 m 1.6 m 0.3 m

2.0 m 0.7 m 3.5 m 8.1 m 4.6 m

Rounding decimals

Write each amount to the nearest pound.

£1.67	£2.83	£1.23	£3.28
£2.00	£3.00	£1.00	£3.00

Write each amount to the nearest pound.

£2.67	£3.18	£6.75	£7.43
£8.28	£8.67	£4.97	£2.43
£4.66	£8.12	£6.08	£5.40
£7.02	£6.74	£7.83	£12.78
£11.64	£10.64	£15.67	£21.37

Write each length to the nearest metre.

1.76 m	4.32 m	6.75 m	3.84 m
7.40 m	3.18 m	7.31 m	9.63 m
5.42 m	12.82 m	18.53 m	16.45 m
10.53 m	20.65 m	17.45 m	14.32 m
12.64 m	19.05 m	15.51 m	27.47 m

Write each amount to the nearest pound or metre.

3.46 m	£2.50	4.50 m	£7.50
12.50 m	18.99 m	£12.50	23.50 m
35.50 m	£61.67	50.50 m	67.50 m
£45.67	£63.50	£89.78	34.50 m
£58.50	£21.56	£95.50	64.50 m

Adding

Write the answer between the lines.

```
    67        39        45
  + 32      + 43      + 26
  ------    ------    ------
    99        82        71
```

Write the answer between the lines.

```
    43        72        56        28        47
  + 25      + 16      + 14      + 15      + 13
  ------    ------    ------    ------    ------


    36        54        84        47        54
  + 15      + 17      + 13      + 16      + 19
  ------    ------    ------    ------    ------


    45        48        64        70        45
  + 15      + 14      + 19      + 14      + 17
  ------    ------    ------    ------    ------


    18        17        14        18        14
  + 33      + 44      + 56      + 44      + 54
  ------    ------    ------    ------    ------


    26        45        74        36        81
  + 36      + 34      + 18      + 17      +  8
  ------    ------    ------    ------    ------


    45        43        57        49        37
  + 35      + 28      + 44      + 37      + 46
  ------    ------    ------    ------    ------
```

Adding

Write the answer between the lines.

37 m	56 m	68 m	49 m	28 m
+ 46 m	+ 36 m	+ 45 m	+ 27 m	+ 36 m

47 km	29 km	56 km	55 km	38 km
+ 44 km	+ 34 km	+ 35 km	+ 37 km	+ 44 km

65 kg	43 kg	52 kg	47 kg	36 kg
+ 27 kg	+ 18 kg	+ 17 kg	+ 27 kg	+ 17 kg

57 g	48 g	44 g	66 g	43 g
+ 42 g	+ 24 g	+ 18 g	+ 27 g	+ 29 g

Write the answer between the lines.

£23.00	£36.00	£75.00	£27.00
+ £18.00	+ £43.00	+ £16.00	+ £38.00

Adding

Write the answer between the lines.

```
  35        18        24
  17        14        16
+ 16      + 17      + 19
-----     -----     -----
  68        49        59
-----     -----     -----
```

Write the answer between the lines.

```
  12        17        15        12        18
  13        10        13        14        10
+ 13      + 11      + 11      + 12      + 11
-----     -----     -----     -----     -----

-----     -----     -----     -----     -----


  17        19        16        12        19
  26        13        21        25        32
+ 12      + 14      + 31      + 33      + 12
-----     -----     -----     -----     -----

-----     -----     -----     -----     -----


  20        30        40        50        60
  32        26        42        21        14
+ 16      + 25      + 25      + 21      +  8
-----     -----     -----     -----     -----

-----     -----     -----     -----     -----


  25        35        45        55        65
  15        25        15        35        15
+  5      +  5      +  5      +  5      +  5
-----     -----     -----     -----     -----

-----     -----     -----     -----     -----


  23        34        45        56        67
  45        32        16        16        12
+ 32      + 13      +  9      +  7      +  8
-----     -----     -----     -----     -----

-----     -----     -----     -----     -----
```

Subtracting

Write the answer between the lines.

```
  57          42          36
-  15       -  16       -  29
  42          26           7
```

Write the answer between the lines.

```
  40          60          70          50          90
-  18       -  23       -  37       -  18       -  27
```

```
  41          62          85          64          71
-  14       -  15       -  37       -  45       -  36
```

```
  45          65          75          95          85
-  18       -  34       -  69       -  49       -  38
```

```
  73          82          74          81          64
-  27       -  38       -  47       -  39       -  47
```

```
  61          52          61          53          73
-  14       -  17       -  19       -  23       -  44
```

```
  70          63          83          53          47
-  26       -   7       -  56       -  36       -  43
```

Subtracting

Write the answer between the lines.

56 m	37 km	58 kg
− 18 m	− 19 km	− 19 kg
38 m	18 km	39 kg

Write the answer between the lines.

45 m	63 m	74 m	82 m	40 m
− 23 m	− 44 m	− 38 m	− 29 m	− 17 m

61 m	81 m	62 m	83 m	43 m
− 27 m	− 36 m	− 27 m	− 36 m	− 17 m

45 m	60 m	73 m	74 m	85 m
− 26 m	− 47 m	− 48 m	− 39 m	− 47 m

Write the answer between the lines.

50 km	37 km	75 km	84 km	90 km
− 28 km	− 18 km	− 39 km	− 29 km	− 37 km

Write the answer between the lines.

68 kg	47 kg	64 kg	79 kg	56 kg
− 39 kg	− 38 kg	− 27 kg	− 27 kg	− 45 kg

Answer Section with Parents' Notes
Key Stage 2
Ages 8–9
Workbook 3

This 8-page section provides answers to all the activities in this book. This will enable you to mark your children's work or can be used by them if they prefer to do their own marking.

The notes for each page help explain the common pitfalls and problems and, where appropriate, give indications as to what practice is needed to ensure your children understand where they have gone wrong.

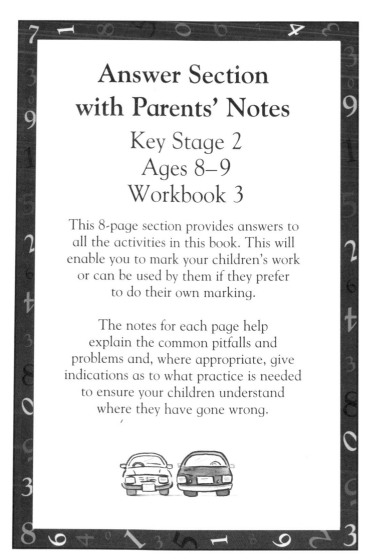

---

2 ⭐ ## Adding and subtracting

Add 100 to 356.	Add 1 000 to 2 376.
456	3 376
Subtract 100 from 5 324.	Subtract 1 000 from 7 296.
5224	6296

Add 100 to each number.

376	476	795	895	646	746	585	685
286	386	57	157	4 312	4412	5 634	5734
12	112	4 789	4889	924	1024	3 903	4003

Add 1 000 to each number.

485	1485	607	1607	37	1037	943	1943
3 587	4587	7 056	8056	5 045	6045	2 907	3907
5 897	6897	9 564	10564	5 499	6499	9 001	10001

Subtract 100 from each number.

364	264	729	629	477	377	765	665
103	3	146	46	1 003	903	599	499
100	0	5 745	5645	3 078	2978	6 107	6007

Subtract 1 000 from each number.

4 734	3734	8 610	7610	5 307	4307	9 362	8362
12 675	11675	4 907	3907	8 445	7445	1 001	1
1 400	400	15 638	14638	20 832	19832	14 056	13056

Children should be aware that adding 100 will increase the digit in the hundreds column by 1 and may also have an effect on the thousands column. This also applies to the process of adding 1 000, and the opposite when subtracting 100 or 1 000.

---

3 ## Dividing by 10 and 100 ⭐

Divide 90 by 10.	Divide 3 400 by 100.
9	34

Divide each number by 10.

60	6	80	8	10	1	50	5
100	10	150	15	230	23	300	30
210	21	170	17	20	2	260	26
40	4	360	36	590	59	730	73
420	42	380	38	820	82	540	54

Divide each number by 100.

300	3	700	7	900	9	100	1
600	6	800	8	1 100	11	1 400	14
1 700	17	1 900	19	2 300	23	2 800	28
3 800	38	4 100	41	8 400	84	9 400	94
6 000	60	1 000	10	7 500	75	5 600	56

Divide each number by 10.

700	70	2 300	230	4 100	410	3 650	365
6 480	648	7 080	708	3 540	354	2 030	203
1 030	103	9 670	967	6 320	632	1 400	140
300	30	900	90	1 020	102	3 660	366
20	2	18 000	1800	13 600	1360	17 890	1789

Many children will give correct answers because they quickly realise that it is just a matter of 'taking off a nought'. They should also realise that this happens because they are finding how many lots of 10 there are in the number given.

---

4 ⭐ ## Negative numbers

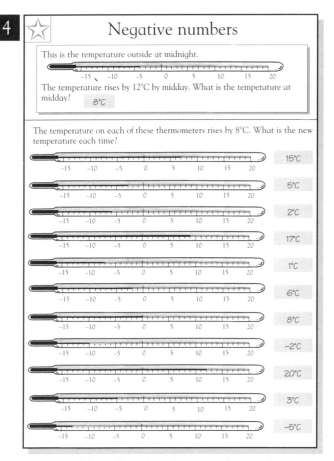

This is the temperature outside at midnight.

The temperature rises by 12°C by midday. What is the temperature at midday? 8°C

The temperature on each of these thermometers rises by 8°C. What is the new temperature each time?

15°C
5°C
2°C
17°C
1°C
6°C
8°C
−2°C
20°C
3°C
−5°C

Year 4 children should understand the word 'rises' in the question and its significance. Though the children may refer to the thermometers, ask them to try to work out one of the answers in their heads to see if they can visualise the problem properly.

Counting in steps ☆

Continue each sequence.

| 11 | 22 | 33 | 44 | 55 | 66 | 77 | 88 |
| 12 | 24 | 36 | 48 | 60 | 72 | 84 | 96 |

Continue each sequence.

12	23	34	45	56	67	78	89
9	21	33	45	57	69	81	93
32	43	54	65	76	87	98	109
2	14	26	38	50	62	74	86
–20	–9	2	13	24	35	46	57
–30	–18	–6	6	18	30	42	54
–41	–30	–19	–8	3	14	25	36
–60	–48	–36	–24	–12	0	12	24

Continue each sequence.

45	34	23	12	1	–10	–21	–32
70	58	46	34	22	10	–2	–14
44	33	22	11	0	–11	–22	–33
48	36	24	12	0	–12	–24	–36
7	–4	–15	–26	–37	–48	–59	–70
14	2	–10	–22	–34	–46	–58	–70
8	–3	–14	–25	–36	–47	–58	–69
10	–2	–14	–26	–38	–50	–62	–74

The questions that cross the zero boundary are most likely to cause problems. Watch out for the 8th sequence. Any mistakes may be remedied by drawing a simple number line, such as that used on the thermometer on the previous page.

☆ Multiples

Circle the multiples of 11.

9   16   ⓐ22   34   ⓑ44   60   ⓒ77   90

Circle the multiples of 12.

14   26   39   ⓓ48   63   ⓔ72   94   100

Circle the multiples of 11.

1	7	⑪	18	24	32	㊹	58
6	13	㉒	34	㊹	54	㊿66	㊿77
⑪	14	21	26	㊿55	㊿88	㊿99	100
20	25	30	35	40	45	50	㊿55
㊿66	26	46	64	㊹	24	62	72
16	24	32	40	48	56	64	72
⑪	㉒	㉝33	㊹	㊿55	㊿66	78	㊿88
96	73	⑪	45	62	㊿77	14	㉝33

Circle the multiples of 12.

4	8	⑫	16	20	㉔	28	32
9	⑫	15	18	21	㉔	27	30
6	⑫	18	㉔	30	㊱36	42	㊽48
8	16	㉔	32	40	㊽48	56	64
9	18	27	㊱36	45	54	63	㉟72
10	20	30	40	50	㊿60	70	80
⑫	㉔	㊱36	㊽48	㊿60	㉟72	㊹84	㊻96
68	56	44	32	20	⑫	0	㊱36

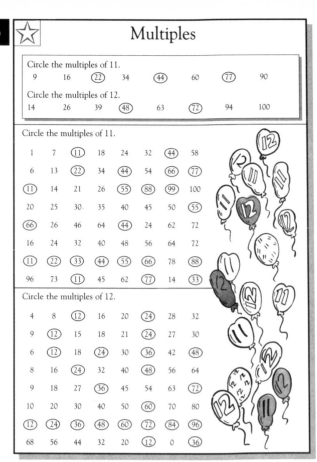

The children should spot the multiples of 11 fairly easily but in the 7th row they might be careless with 78. The multiples of 12 are not so easy to spot and it may be worthwhile seeing if the children can extend beyond the ones in the 7th row.

Square numbers ☆

The square has two rows and two columns. It is 2^2.

2^2 is the same as
$2 \times 2 = 4$

How many dots are there? **4**

Draw a picture like the one above to show each of these numbers squared.

3^2 How many dots are there? **9**

4^2 How many dots are there? **16**

5^2 How many dots are there? **25**

6^2 How many dots are there? **36**

7^2 How many dots are there? **49**

8^2 How many dots are there? **64**

9^2 How many dots are there? **81**

10^2 How many dots are there? **100**

This is a traditional way of showing square numbers but many children will pick up the idea of 'multiplying the number by itself' fairly quickly. If the children pick up the idea do not make them draw the dots but talk through the work with them instead.

☆ Fractions and decimals

Write each fraction as a decimal.
$\frac{1}{2}$ = **0.5** $\frac{1}{10}$ = **0.1**

Write each decimal as a fraction.
0.25 = **$\frac{1}{4}$**

Write each fraction as a decimal.

$\frac{1}{4}$	**0.25**	$\frac{1}{2}$	**0.5**	$\frac{3}{4}$	**0.75**	$\frac{1}{5}$	**0.2**
$\frac{2}{5}$	**0.4**	$\frac{3}{5}$	**0.6**	$\frac{4}{5}$	**0.8**	$\frac{1}{10}$	**0.1**
$\frac{2}{10}$	**0.2**	$\frac{3}{10}$	**0.3**	$\frac{4}{10}$	**0.4**	$\frac{5}{10}$	**0.5**
$\frac{6}{10}$	**0.6**	$\frac{7}{10}$	**0.7**	$\frac{8}{10}$	**0.8**	$\frac{9}{10}$	**0.9**

Write each decimal as a different fraction.

0.8	**$\frac{8}{10}$**	0.5	**$\frac{5}{10}$**	0.3	**$\frac{3}{10}$**	0.4	**$\frac{2}{5}$**
0.25	**$\frac{1}{4}$**	0.7	**$\frac{7}{10}$**	0.2	**$\frac{1}{5}$**	0.75	**$\frac{3}{4}$**
0.2	**$\frac{2}{10}$**	0.6	**$\frac{6}{10}$**	0.5	**$\frac{1}{2}$**	0.8	**$\frac{4}{5}$**
0.1	**$\frac{1}{10}$**	0.4	**$\frac{4}{10}$**	0.6	**$\frac{3}{5}$**	0.9	**$\frac{9}{10}$**

Write the answer in the box.

Which two of the fractions above are the same as 0.5? **$\frac{5}{10}$ $\frac{1}{2}$**

Which two of the fractions above are the same as 0.8? **$\frac{8}{10}$ $\frac{4}{5}$**

Which two of the fractions above are the same as 0.6? **$\frac{6}{10}$ $\frac{3}{5}$**

Which two of the fractions above are the same as 0.2? **$\frac{1}{5}$ $\frac{2}{10}$**

Which two of the fractions above are the same as 0.4? **$\frac{4}{10}$ $\frac{2}{5}$**

In the 3rd section children are asked to give the same decimal in two different ways and they may choose to write either one first. They may not have been told about equivalent fractions, which is what many of these are. This may therefore be worth a discussion.

Fractions of shapes ☆

Shade $\frac{3}{5}$ of each shape.

Shade $\frac{4}{5}$ of each shape.

Shade the amount shown of each shape.

Two-fifths

Four-fifths

Three-tenths

Seven-tenths

Three-fifths

Nine-tenths

Knowledge of equivalence of fractions is being tested in some of these questions although the children may not know it by that name. For example, when $\frac{4}{5}$ of ten sections needs to be shaded, does the child recognise that $\frac{4}{5}$ of 10 is 8?

Ordering decimals

Write each row in order starting with the smallest.

| 1.7 m | 1.3 m | 1.5 m | 1.9 m | 1.3 m | 1.5 m | 1.7 m | 1.9 m |
| 5.3 m | 2.8 m | 3.9 m | 1.6 m | 1.6 m | 2.8 m | 3.9 m | 5.3 m |

Write each row in order starting with the smallest.

2.4 m	2.8 m	2.1 m	2.6 m	2.9 m	2.1 m	2.4 m	2.6 m	2.8 m	2.9 m
5.2 m	5.7 m	5.1 m	5.8 m	5.3 m	5.1 m	5.2 m	5.3 m	5.7 m	5.8 m
1.4 m	1.7 m	1.8 m	1.1 m	1.9 m	1.1 m	1.4 m	1.7 m	1.8 m	1.9 m
3.8 m	3.6 m	3.4 m	3.2 m	3.1 m	3.1 m	3.2 m	3.4 m	3.6 m	3.8 m
7.5 m	7.3 m	7.9 m	7.2 m	7.8 m	7.2 m	7.3 m	7.5 m	7.8 m	7.9 m
4.3 m	4.6 m	4.0 m	4.2 m	4.8 m	4.0 m	4.2 m	4.3 m	4.6 m	4.8 m
6.9 m	6.0 m	6.4 m	6.2 m	6.7 m	6.0 m	6.2 m	6.4 m	6.7 m	6.9 m
10.6 m	10.3 m	10.8 m	10.5 m	10.0 m	10.0 m	10.3 m	10.5 m	10.6 m	10.8 m
7.4 m	6.4 m	9.4 m	2.4 m	8.4 m	2.4 m	6.4 m	7.4 m	8.4 m	9.4 m
3.7 m	6.7 m	7.7 m	2.7 m	9.7 m	2.7 m	3.7 m	6.7 m	7.7 m	9.7 m
4.5 m	1.5 m	3.5 m	8.5 m	10.5 m	1.5 m	3.5 m	4.5 m	8.5 m	10.5 m
6.9 m	1.9 m	8.9 m	9.9 m	5.9 m	1.9 m	5.9 m	6.9 m	8.9 m	9.9 m
0.6 m	2.6 m	1.6 m	6.6 m	9.6 m	0.6 m	1.6 m	2.6 m	6.6 m	9.6 m
3.5 m	1.8 m	2.7 m	4.3 m	7.9 m	1.8 m	2.7 m	3.5 m	4.3 m	7.9 m
7.6 m	2.3 m	4.9 m	1.6 m	0.3 m	0.3 m	1.6 m	2.3 m	4.9 m	7.6 m
2.0 m	0.7 m	3.5 m	8.1 m	4.6 m	0.7 m	2.0 m	3.5 m	4.6 m	8.1 m

Children should successfully put the amounts in the first few examples in order as they all begin with the same number. In the later examples, they may need to be reminded that the digits in the tens/units columns must be dealt with before those in the first decimal place.

Rounding decimals ☆

Write each amount to the nearest pound.

| £1.67 | £2.83 | £1.23 | £3.28 |
| £2.00 | £3.00 | £1.00 | £3.00 |

Write each amount to the nearest pound.

£2.67	£3.00	£3.18	£3.00	£6.75	£7.00	£7.43	£7.00
£8.28	£8.00	£8.67	£9.00	£4.97	£5.00	£2.43	£2.00
£4.66	£5.00	£8.12	£8.00	£6.08	£6.00	£5.40	£5.00
£7.02	£7.00	£6.74	£7.00	£7.83	£8.00	£12.78	£13.00
£11.64	£12.00	£10.64	£11.00	£15.67	£16.00	£21.37	£21.00

Write each length to the nearest metre.

1.76 m	2 m	4.32 m	4 m	6.75 m	7 m	3.84 m	4 m
7.40 m	7 m	3.18 m	3 m	7.31 m	7 m	9.63 m	10 m
5.42 m	5 m	12.82 m	13 m	18.53 m	19 m	16.45 m	16 m
10.53 m	11 m	20.65 m	21 m	17.45 m	17 m	14.32 m	14 m
12.64 m	13 m	19.05 m	19 m	15.51 m	16 m	27.47 m	27 m

Write each amount to the nearest whole pound or metre.

3.46 m	3 m	£2.50	£3.00	4.50 m	5 m	£7.50	£8.00
12.50 m	13 m	18.99 m	19 m	£12.50	£13.00	23.50 m	24 m
35.50 m	36 m	£61.67	£62.00	50.50 m	51 m	67.50 m	68 m
£45.67	£46.00	£63.50	£64.00	£89.78	£90.00	34.50 m	35 m
£58.50	£59.00	£21.56	£22.00	£95.50	£96.00	64.50 m	65 m

The children should recognise the importance of the 50p or 50 cm border when rounding either up or down. Some of the questions in the 3rd section are half way between whole units and children should know that the convention is to round up when this occurs.

Adding

Write the answers between the lines.

67	39	45
+ 32	+ 43	+ 26
99	82	71

Write the answers between the lines.

43	72	56	28	47
+ 25	+ 16	+ 14	+ 15	+ 13
68	88	70	43	60

36	54	84	47	54
+ 15	+ 17	+ 13	+ 16	+ 19
51	71	97	63	73

45	48	64	70	45
+ 15	+ 14	+ 19	+ 14	+ 17
60	62	83	84	62

18	17	14	18	14
+ 33	+ 44	+ 56	+ 44	+ 54
51	61	70	62	68

26	45	74	36	81
+ 36	+ 34	+ 18	+ 17	+ 8
62	79	92	53	89

45	43	57	49	37
+ 35	+ 28	+ 44	+ 37	+ 46
80	71	101	86	83

Most of the sums require carrying across into the tens columns. Parents should observe how children deal with those sums that do not require carrying. If they hesitate, parents should ask them what they are thinking.

Adding ☆

Write the answer between the lines.

35 m	74 m	46 m
+ 25 m	+ 18 m	+ 36 m
60 m	**92 m**	**82 m**

Write the answer between the lines.

37 m	56 m	68 m	49 m	28 m
+ 46 m	+ 36 m	+ 45 m	+ 27 m	+ 36 m
83 m	**92 m**	**113 m**	**76 m**	**64 m**

47 km	29 km	56 km	55 km	38 km
+ 44 km	+ 34 km	+ 35 km	+ 37 km	+ 44 km
91 km	**63 km**	**91 km**	**92 km**	**82 km**

65 kg	43 kg	52 kg	47 kg	36 kg
+ 27 kg	+ 18 kg	+ 17 kg	+ 27 kg	+ 17 kg
92 kg	**61 kg**	**69 kg**	**74 kg**	**53 kg**

57 g	48 g	44 g	66 g	43 g
+ 42 g	+ 24 g	+ 18 g	+ 27 g	+ 29 g
99 g	**72 g**	**62 g**	**93 g**	**72 g**

Write the answer between the lines.

£23.00	£36.00	£75.00	£27.00
+ £18.00	+ £43.00	+ £16.00	+ £38.00
£41.00	**£79.00**	**£91.00**	**£65.00**

Make sure that the children carry across to the tens column when necessary. A few sums do not need carrying so, as with the last page, watch to see if this confuses the child. If so, talk it through with them.

☆ Adding

Write the answer between the lines.

35	18	24
17	14	16
+ 16	+ 17	+ 19
68	**49**	**59**

Write the answer between the lines.

12	17	15	12	18
13	10	13	14	10
+ 13	+ 11	+ 11	+ 12	+ 11
38	**38**	**39**	**38**	**39**

17	19	16	12	19
26	13	21	25	32
+ 12	+ 14	+ 31	+ 33	+ 12
55	**46**	**68**	**70**	**63**

20	30	40	50	60
32	26	42	21	14
+ 16	+ 25	+ 25	+ 21	+ 8
68	**81**	**107**	**92**	**82**

25	35	45	55	65
15	25	15	35	15
+ 5	+ 5	+ 5	+ 5	+ 5
45	**65**	**65**	**95**	**85**

23	34	45	56	67
45	32	16	16	12
+ 32	+ 13	+ 9	+ 7	+ 8
100	**79**	**70**	**79**	**87**

Children should try to develop strategies to work these sums out. One method is to add up the smaller two amounts and then add on the third amount. Some children look for two of the units resulting in 10 and add those amounts first.

Subtracting ☆

Write the answer between the lines.

57	42	36
− 15	− 16	− 29
42	**26**	**7**

Write the answer between the lines.

40	60	70	50	90
− 18	− 23	− 37	− 18	− 27
22	**37**	**33**	**32**	**63**

41	62	85	64	71
− 14	− 15	− 37	− 45	− 36
27	**47**	**48**	**19**	**35**

45	65	75	95	85
− 18	− 34	− 69	− 49	− 38
27	**31**	**6**	**46**	**47**

73	82	74	81	64
− 27	− 38	− 47	− 39	− 47
46	**44**	**27**	**42**	**17**

61	52	61	53	73
− 14	− 17	− 19	− 23	− 44
47	**35**	**42**	**30**	**29**

70	63	83	53	47
− 26	− 7	− 56	− 36	− 43
44	**56**	**27**	**17**	**4**

Most of the subtraction sums require 'borrowing' or 'stealing' from the tens column, also known as 'exchanging'. Parents should talk through the methods of subtraction the children are using to make sure they are logical, accurate, and quick.

☆ Subtracting

Write the answer between the lines.

56 m	37 km	58 kg
− 18 m	− 19 km	− 19 kg
38 m	**18 km**	**39 kg**

Write the answer between the lines.

45 m	63 m	74 m	82 m	40 m
− 23 m	− 44 m	− 38 m	− 29 m	− 17 m
22 m	**19 m**	**36 m**	**53 m**	**23 m**

61 m	81 m	62 m	83 m	43 m
− 27 m	− 36 m	− 27 m	− 36 m	− 17 m
34 m	**45 m**	**35 m**	**47 m**	**26 m**

45 m	60 m	73 m	74 m	85 m
− 26 m	− 47 m	− 48 m	− 39 m	− 47 m
19 m	**13 m**	**25 m**	**35 m**	**38 m**

Write the answer between the lines.

50 km	37 km	75 km	84 km	90 km
− 28 km	− 18 km	− 39 km	− 29 km	− 37 km
22 km	**19 km**	**36 km**	**55 km**	**53 km**

Write the answer between the lines.

68 kg	47 kg	64 kg	79 kg	56 kg
− 39 kg	− 38 kg	− 27 kg	− 27 kg	− 45 kg
29 kg	**9 kg**	**37 kg**	**52 kg**	**11 kg**

Children who are normally good at subtraction can be confused when there is a zero on the top line in the units column as, for example, with the 5th answer. Any problems with these sums should be discussed.

Real life problems

Work out the sum and then write the answers.

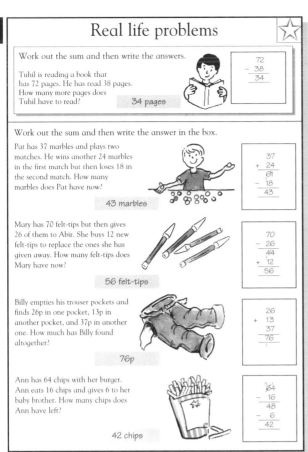

Tuhil is reading a book that has 72 pages. He has read 38 pages. How many more pages does Tuhil have to read?

```
   72
 - 38
   34
```

34 pages

Work out the sum and then write the answer in the box.

Pat has 37 marbles and plays two matches. He wins another 24 marbles in the first match but then loses 18 in the second match. How many marbles does Pat have now?

```
   37
 + 24
   61
 - 18
   43
```

43 marbles

Mary has 70 felt-tips but then gives 26 of them to Abir. She buys 12 new felt-tips to replace the ones she has given away. How many felt-tips does Mary have now?

```
   70
 - 26
   44
 + 12
   56
```

56 felt-tips

Billy empties his trouser pockets and finds 26p in one pocket, 13p in another pocket, and 37p in another one. How much has Billy found altogether?

```
   26
 + 13
   37
   76
```

76p

Ann has 64 chips with her burger. Ann eats 16 chips and gives 6 to her baby brother. How many chips does Ann have left?

```
   64
 - 16
   48
 -  6
   42
```

42 chips

Here the children work out which operation needs to be used. Although most children find simple symbolic problems like 12 + 16 easy, problems in a word context often confuse them. Parents should talk through any problems answered incorrectly.

Multiplying

Write the answer between the lines.

27	53	36	19
x 5	x 4	x 3	x 4
135	212	108	76

Write the answer between the lines.

26	43	67	18	74
x 4	x 4	x 4	x 4	x 4
104	172	268	72	296

19	41	58	32	94
x 3	x 3	x 3	x 3	x 3
57	123	174	96	282

33	49	67	28	63
x 5	x 5	x 5	x 5	x 5
165	245	335	140	315

64	85	94	57	78
x 2	x 2	x 2	x 2	x 2
128	170	188	114	156

15	53	64	85	72
x 6	x 6	x 6	x 6	x 6
90	318	384	510	432

37	85	51	84	47
x 8	x 8	x 8	x 8	x 8
296	680	408	672	376

Most of the sums require carrying across from the units to the tens column. Each row of five sums is multiplied by the same number so these sums can also be used to check the children's knowledge of particular times tables.

Multiplying

Write the answer between the lines.

24	75	58	17
x 4	x 6	x 4	x 5
96	450	232	85

Write the answer between the lines.

43	50	37	29	16
x 7	x 7	x 7	x 7	x 7
301	350	259	203	112

27	58	36	14	61
x 9	x 9	x 9	x 9	x 9
243	522	324	126	549

53	37	49	58	67
x 10	x 10	x 10	x 10	x 10
530	370	490	580	670

37	47	87	17	97
x 4	x 5	x 6	x 7	x 8
148	235	522	119	776

58	38	78	28	18
x 6	x 7	x 8	x 9	x 10
348	266	624	252	180

49	29	59	89	69
x 5	x 6	x 7	x 8	x 9
245	174	413	712	621

Make sure that the children carry across any numbers that need to go into the tens column. Pay attention to any groups of sums being incorrect when multiplied by the same number, i.e. 7 or 8. This will indicate a weakness in the knowledge of that times table.

Dividing

Write the answer in the box.

24 ÷ 7 = **3 r 3**   5 ⟌ 21 **4 r 1**   43 ÷ 8 = **5 r 3**

Write the answer in the box.

27 ÷ 3 = **9**	14 ÷ 3 = **4 r 2**	23 ÷ 3 = **7 r 2**
7 ÷ 3 = **2 r 1**	31 ÷ 4 = **7 r 3**	14 ÷ 4 = **3 r 2**
38 ÷ 4 = **9 r 2**	4 ÷ 4 = **1**	42 ÷ 5 = **8 r 2**
23 ÷ 5 = **4 r 3**	15 ÷ 5 = **3**	27 ÷ 5 = **5 r 2**
47 ÷ 6 = **7 r 5**	35 ÷ 5 = **7**	46 ÷ 5 = **9 r 1**
24 ÷ 5 = **4 r 4**	42 ÷ 7 = **6**	60 ÷ 7 = **8 r 4**

Write the answer in the box.

4 r 2	**5 r 6**	**2 r 5**	**7**	**3**
8 ⟌ 34	8 ⟌ 46	8 ⟌ 21	8 ⟌ 56	9 ⟌ 27
5 r 1	**6 r 4**	**8 r 2**	**7 r 1**	**10 r 1**
9 ⟌ 46	9 ⟌ 58	9 ⟌ 74	2 ⟌ 15	2 ⟌ 21
1 r 1	**8**	**5 r 2**	**7 r 2**	**10**
2 ⟌ 3	2 ⟌ 16	3 ⟌ 17	3 ⟌ 23	3 ⟌ 30
8	**3 r 1**	**6**	**7 r 3**	**10 r 3**
3 ⟌ 24	4 ⟌ 13	4 ⟌ 24	4 ⟌ 31	4 ⟌ 43

Write the answer in the box.

45 ÷ 8 = **5 r 5**	73 ÷ 8 = **9 r 1**	56 ÷ 8 = **7**
73 ÷ 9 = **8 r 1**	41 ÷ 9 = **4 r 5**	50 ÷ 9 = **5 r 5**
54 ÷ 10 = **5 r 4**	89 ÷ 10 = **8 r 9**	42 ÷ 10 = **4 r 2**

Children very often think that division sums are 'teacher's tricks' and are almost bound to have remainders to make them work harder! They seem puzzled by those that work out exactly.

Dividing ⭐

Write the answer in the box.

31 ÷ 4 = [7 r 3]   [2 r 5] / 6)17   31 ÷ 9 = [3 r 4]

Write the answer in the box.

46 ÷ 9 = 5 r 1	28 ÷ 7 = 4	45 ÷ 9 = 5
74 ÷ 8 = 9 r 2	32 ÷ 3 = 10 r 2	45 ÷ 7 = 6 r 3
61 ÷ 7 = 8 r 5	65 ÷ 9 = 7 r 2	12 ÷ 9 = 1 r 3
17 ÷ 4 = 4 r 1	24 ÷ 6 = 4	36 ÷ 6 = 6
37 ÷ 8 = 4 r 5	37 ÷ 9 = 4 r 1	37 ÷ 10 = 3 r 7
37 ÷ 6 = 6 r 1	54 ÷ 6 = 9	54 ÷ 7 = 7 r 5

Write the answer in the box.

6 r 3 / 7)45	7 / 8)56	4 r 7 / 9)43	5 / 6)30	3 r 5 / 10)35
1 r 3 / 9)12	6 r 2 / 5)32	6 r 2 / 7)44	1 r 1 / 7)8	4 r 2 / 8)34
5 r 3 / 10)53	8 r 4 / 9)76	10 r 4 / 5)54	6 r 1 / 7)43	9 / 3)27
7 / 6)42	9 / 7)63	4 r 6 / 9)42	10 r 3 / 8)83	9 r 4 / 5)49

Write the answer in the box.

8 ÷ 6 = 1 r 2	12 ÷ 10 = 1 r 2	11 ÷ 9 = 1 r 2
13 ÷ 10 = 1 r 3	17 ÷ 7 = 2 r 3	23 ÷ 8 = 2 r 7
70 ÷ 10 = 7	70 ÷ 7 = 10	54 ÷ 6 = 9

As with the previous page, some of these problems work out exactly and others do not. Look out for the 3rd section where the numbers are small. Children sometimes lose track of 'which number is going into which' when both numbers are about the same size.

⭐ Choose the operation

Write either x or ÷ in the box.

6 [x] 7 = 42   24 [÷] 6 = 4   10 [÷] 2 = 5

Write either x or ÷ in the box.

35 ÷ 7 = 5	35 ÷ 5 = 7	7 x 5 = 35
5 x 7 = 35	6 x 9 = 54	54 ÷ 6 = 9
9 x 6 = 54	54 ÷ 9 = 6	32 ÷ 4 = 8
4 x 8 = 32	8 x 4 = 32	32 ÷ 8 = 4
4 x 9 = 36	36 ÷ 4 = 9	9 x 4 = 36
36 ÷ 9 = 4	80 ÷ 8 = 10	8 x 10 = 80
7 x 9 = 63	63 ÷ 7 = 9	63 ÷ 9 = 7
9 x 7 = 63	9 x 9 = 81	81 ÷ 9 = 9
64 ÷ 8 = 8	8 x 8 = 64	25 ÷ 5 = 5
5 x 5 = 25	16 ÷ 4 = 4	4 x 4 = 16
7 x 7 = 49	49 ÷ 7 = 7	3 x 3 = 9
9 ÷ 3 = 3	100 ÷ 10 = 10	10 x 10 = 100
50 ÷ 10 = 5	5 x 8 = 40	40 ÷ 4 = 10
20 ÷ 5 = 4	4 x 10 = 40	36 ÷ 6 = 6
3 x 7 = 21	21 ÷ 3 = 7	7 x 4 = 28
14 x 10 = 140	140 ÷ 2 = 70	70 ÷ 10 = 7
42 ÷ 6 = 7	7 x 10 = 70	72 ÷ 8 = 9
50 ÷ 5 = 10	20 ÷ 4 = 5	3 x 8 = 24

Much of this work is recalling times tables knowledge. See how quickly and comfortably children can move between multiplying and dividing.

Real life problems ⭐

Write the answer in the box.

There are 8 ink cartridges in each packet. How many cartridges will there be in 6 packets?   8 x 6 = 48   48 cartridges

Write the answer in the box.

Ian shares 50 oranges equally between 6 elephants and gives the remainder to the giraffes. How many oranges do the giraffes receive?   8 r 2 / 6)50   2 oranges

There are 9 children at a birthday party and each child has 4 chocolate cakes. How many chocolate cakes do the children have altogether?   9 x 4 = 36   36 cakes

Ben has 60 building bricks and puts them in piles of 7. How many piles of 7 can Ben make?   8 r 4 / 7)60   8 piles

Katy has seven 10p coins, four 5p coins, and two 2p coins. How much does she have altogether?   10 x 7 = 70 / 4 x 5 = 20 + / 2 x 2 = 4 / 94   94p

The dog buries four bones in each hole. The dog has 36 bones. How many holes must the dog dig?   9 / 4)36   9 holes

Questions 1 and 3 do not require answers in the usual form of 'x remainder y' and this may cause confusion. Children need to read the question carefully to find out exactly what is required. Hopefully, they should be able to answer the 4th problem in their heads`.

⭐ Perimeter

Write the perimeter of this shape in the answer box.

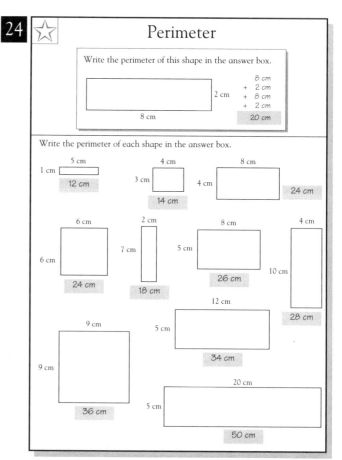

8 cm / 2 cm / 8 cm   8 cm + 2 cm + 8 cm + 2 cm   20 cm

Write the perimeter of each shape in the answer box.

5 cm, 1 cm → 12 cm
4 cm, 3 cm → 14 cm
8 cm, 4 cm → 24 cm
6 cm, 6 cm → 24 cm
2 cm, 7 cm → 18 cm
8 cm, 5 cm → 26 cm
4 cm, 10 cm → 28 cm
9 cm, 9 cm → 36 cm
12 cm, 5 cm → 34 cm
20 cm, 5 cm → 50 cm

Explain that perimeter is the distance around the edge of a shape. There are a few methods used to find the perimeter of a square or rectangle: add two different sides together then double the number; double each side, then add them together; add each side one by one in sequence.

Area

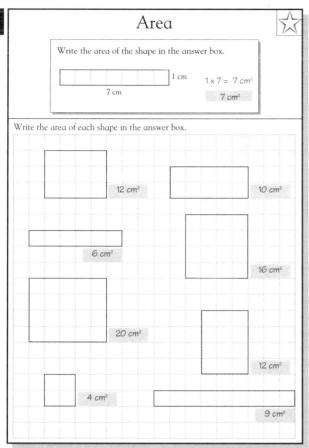

Write the area of the shape in the answer box.

1 cm
7 cm
1 × 7 = 7 cm²
7 cm²

Write the area of each shape in the answer box.

12 cm²
10 cm²
6 cm²
16 cm²
20 cm²
12 cm²
4 cm²
9 cm²

Since the area of a shape is the amount of space inside it, the number of squares inside each shape is the answer. Children should realise that multiplying one side by the other will give the same result more quickly. This does not work with shapes such as triangles.

Area

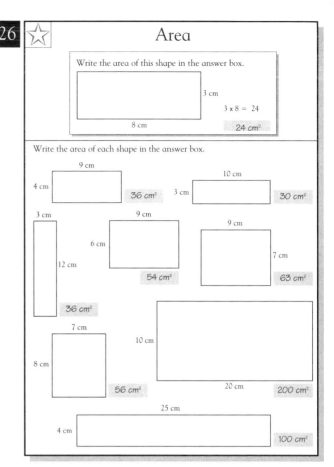

Write the area of this shape in the answer box.

3 cm
8 cm
3 × 8 = 24
24 cm²

Write the area of each shape in the answer box.

9 cm, 4 cm — 36 cm²
10 cm, 3 cm — 30 cm²
3 cm, 9 cm, 6 cm, 12 cm — 54 cm²
9 cm, 7 cm — 63 cm²
36 cm²
7 cm, 8 cm — 56 cm²
10 cm, 20 cm — 200 cm²
25 cm, 4 cm — 100 cm²

Following on from the last page, this page requires children to find the areas by multiplying the sides together. If they are unsure, you could sketch in squares on the shapes to help.

Problems using time

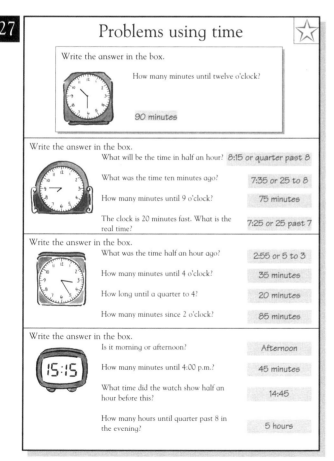

Write the answer in the box.

How many minutes until twelve o'clock?

90 minutes

Write the answer in the box.

What will be the time in half an hour? **8:15 or quarter past 8**

What was the time ten minutes ago? **7:35 or 25 to 8**

How many minutes until 9 o'clock? **75 minutes**

The clock is 20 minutes fast. What is the real time? **7:25 or 25 past 7**

Write the answer in the box.

What was the time half an hour ago? **2:55 or 5 to 3**

How many minutes until 4 o'clock? **35 minutes**

How long until a quarter to 4? **20 minutes**

How many minutes since 2 o'clock? **85 minutes**

Write the answer in the box.

Is it morning or afternoon? **Afternoon**

How many minutes until 4:00 p.m.? **45 minutes**

What time did the watch show half an hour before this? **14:45**

How many hours until quarter past 8 in the evening? **5 hours**

Although children of this age can usually read and write the time from a clock, their deeper understanding is tested here. Problems are best dealt with by using a large kitchen clock. You can move hands around to illustrate questions.

Reading timetables

	Otterbourne	Compton	Badger Farm	Winchester
Redline Bus	8.00	8.05	8.15	8.25
Wincarry	8.05	No stop	8.12	8.20
Sean's taxi	8.30	8.35	8.45	8.55
Transtrax	8.07	No stop	No stop	8.15

The timetable shows the times it takes to travel using different transport companies between Otterbourne and Winchester.

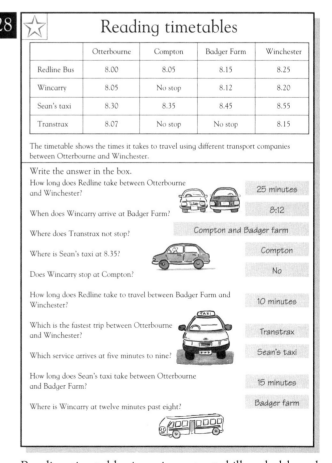

Write the answer in the box.

How long does Redline take between Otterbourne and Winchester? **25 minutes**

When does Wincarry arrive at Badger Farm? **8:12**

Where does Transtrax not stop? **Compton and Badger farm**

Where is Sean's taxi at 8.35? **Compton**

Does Wincarry stop at Compton? **No**

How long does Redline take to travel between Badger Farm and Winchester? **10 minutes**

Which is the fastest trip between Otterbourne and Winchester? **Transtrax**

Which service arrives at five minutes to nine? **Sean's taxi**

How long does Sean's taxi take between Otterbourne and Badger Farm? **15 minutes**

Where is Wincarry at twelve minutes past eight? **Badger farm**

Reading timetables is an important skill and although children should find this exercise fairly straightforward, it is a good starting point to check that children are gaining information logically. Ask the children how they are finding the information.

29 — Mode and median

Write the mode and the median of this row in the boxes.

4	2	2	1	6	3	2

The mode is **2**   The median is **2**

Write the mode of each row in the box.

2	3	7	4	2	7	2	1	**2**
7	4	1	4	8	5	3	4	**4**
5	3	5	3	5	3	4	5	**5**
7	5	9	7	2	4	8	6	**7**
4	3	4	3	4	3	4	5	**4**
0	4	2	7	3	8	2	9	**2**
3	2	1	2	2	3	2	3	**2**
8	3	6	3	8	2	8	4	**8**

Write the median of each row in the box.

4	8	6	3	9	6	7	**6**
5	9	2	6	9	1	4	**5**
6	3	8	6	1	7	6	**6**
3	8	6	7	5	9	4	**6**
1	8	3	4	2	6	5	**4**
9	5	8	6	4	7	9	**7**
2	5	2	3	1	2	3	**2**
6	3	7	4	5	8	6	**6**

Most teachers tell children to remember mode as 'most' and this helps in sorting out between median and mode. Median is the middle number if the numbers are in order, and in groups of 7 numbers it would be the 4th one.

30 — Nets of 3D shapes

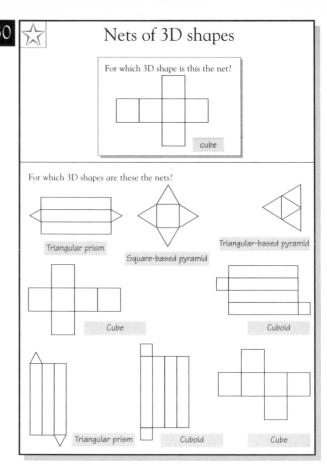

For which 3D shape is this the net?

cube

For which 3D shapes are these the nets?

Triangular prism

Square-based pyramid

Triangular-based pyramid

Cube

Cuboid

Triangular prism

Cuboid

Cube

Most children are familiar with the shapes of nets although they can find it more difficult to draw them. Some shapes, like the cube, have more than one net and it can be an interesting exercise to ask children to find as many different nets for the cube as they can.

31 — Nets of 3D shapes

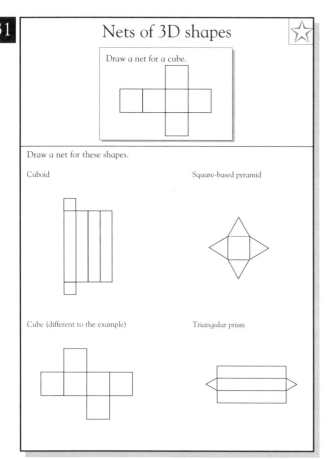

Draw a net for a cube.

Draw a net for these shapes.

Cuboid

Square-based pyramid

Cube (different to the example)

Triangular prism

Each of these shapes has a number of different nets and it may be that the one the child has drawn is not the one shown. However, if in doubt, ask the children to cut out their net and see if it works. Complete this page without referring to the previous page!

32 — Co-ordinates

Look at the grid and then answer the questions below.

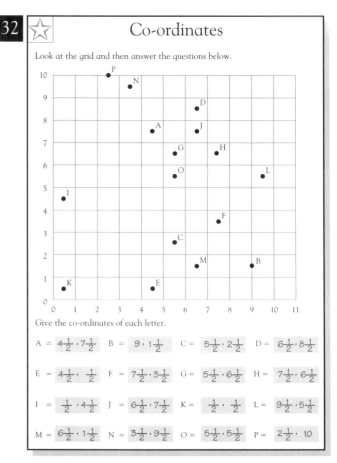

Give the co-ordinates of each letter.

A = $4\frac{1}{2} \cdot 7\frac{1}{2}$ B = $9 \cdot 1\frac{1}{2}$ C = $5\frac{1}{2} \cdot 2\frac{1}{2}$ D = $6\frac{1}{2} \cdot 8\frac{1}{2}$

E = $4\frac{1}{2} \cdot \frac{1}{2}$ F = $7\frac{1}{2} \cdot 3\frac{1}{2}$ G = $5\frac{1}{2} \cdot 6\frac{1}{2}$ H = $7\frac{1}{2} \cdot 6\frac{1}{2}$

I = $\frac{1}{2} \cdot 4\frac{1}{2}$ J = $6\frac{1}{2} \cdot 7\frac{1}{2}$ K = $\frac{1}{2} \cdot \frac{1}{2}$ L = $9\frac{1}{2} \cdot 5\frac{1}{2}$

M = $6\frac{1}{2} \cdot 1\frac{1}{2}$ N = $3\frac{1}{2} \cdot 9\frac{1}{2}$ O = $5\frac{1}{2} \cdot 5\frac{1}{2}$ P = $2\frac{1}{2} \cdot 10$

Watch out for accuracy of half-squares especially when both co-ordinates involve halves. Check that the children always use the first co-ordinate as the across value and the second co-ordinate as the up value.

Real life problems

Work out the sum and then write the answer.

Tuhil is reading a book that
has 72 pages. He has read 38 pages.
How many more pages does
Tuhil have to read?

34 pages

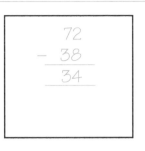

72
− 38
34

Work out the sum and then write the answer in the box.

Pat has 37 marbles and plays two
matches. He wins another 24 marbles
in the first match but then loses 18 in
the second match. How many
marbles does Pat have now?

Mary has 70 felt-tips but then gives
26 of them to Abir. She buys 12 new
felt-tips to replace the ones she has
given away. How many felt-tips does
Mary have now?

Billy empties his trouser pockets and
finds 26p in one pocket, 13p in
another pocket, and 37p in another
one. How much has Billy found
altogether?

Ann has 64 chips with her burger.
Ann eats 16 chips and gives 6 to her
baby brother. How many chips does
Ann have left?

Multiplying

Write the answer between the lines.

27	53	36	19
x 5	x 4	x 3	x 4
135	212	108	76

Write the answer between the lines.

26	43	67	18	74
x 4	x 4	x 4	x 4	x 4

19	41	58	32	94
x 3	x 3	x 3	x 3	x 3

33	49	67	28	63
x 5	x 5	x 5	x 5	x 5

64	85	94	57	78
x 2	x 2	x 2	x 2	x 2

15	53	64	85	72
x 6	x 6	x 6	x 6	x 6

37	85	51	84	47
x 8	x 8	x 8	x 8	x 8

Multiplying

Write the answer between the lines.

24	75	58	17
x 4	x 6	x 4	x 5
96	450	232	85

Write the answer between the lines.

43	50	37	29	16
x 7	x 7	x 7	x 7	x 7

27	58	36	14	61
x 9	x 9	x 9	x 9	x 9

53	37	49	58	67
x 10	x 10	x 10	x 10	x 10

37	47	87	17	97
x 4	x 5	x 6	x 7	x 8

58	38	78	28	18
x 6	x 7	x 8	x 9	x 10

49	29	59	89	69
x 5	x 6	x 7	x 8	x 9

Dividing

Write the answer in the box.

$24 \div 7 =$ 3 r 3   4 r 1 $43 \div 8 =$ 5 r 3

5 ⟌ 21

Write the answer in the box.

$27 \div 3 =$	$14 \div 3 =$	$23 \div 3 =$
$7 \div 3 =$	$31 \div 4 =$	$14 \div 4 =$
$38 \div 4 =$	$4 \div 4 =$	$42 \div 5 =$
$23 \div 5 =$	$15 \div 5 =$	$27 \div 5 =$
$47 \div 6 =$	$35 \div 5 =$	$46 \div 5 =$
$24 \div 5 =$	$42 \div 7 =$	$60 \div 7 =$

Write the answer in the box.

8 ⟌ 34	8 ⟌ 46	8 ⟌ 21	8 ⟌ 56	9 ⟌ 27
9 ⟌ 46	9 ⟌ 58	9 ⟌ 74	2 ⟌ 15	2 ⟌ 21
2 ⟌ 3	2 ⟌ 16	3 ⟌ 17	3 ⟌ 23	3 ⟌ 30
3 ⟌ 24	4 ⟌ 13	4 ⟌ 24	4 ⟌ 31	4 ⟌ 43

Write the answer in the box.

$45 \div 8 =$	$73 \div 8 =$	$56 \div 8 =$
$73 \div 9 =$	$41 \div 9 =$	$50 \div 9 =$
$54 \div 10 =$	$89 \div 10 =$	$42 \div 10 =$

Dividing

Write the answer in the box.

$31 \div 4 =$ 　7 r 3 　　　　2 r 5 　　$31 \div 9 =$ 　3 r 4

$6 \overline{)17}$

Write the answer in the box.

$46 \div 9 =$ 　　　　$28 \div 7 =$ 　　　　$45 \div 9 =$

$74 \div 8 =$ 　　　　$32 \div 3 =$ 　　　　$45 \div 7 =$

$61 \div 7 =$ 　　　　$65 \div 9 =$ 　　　　$12 \div 9 =$

$17 \div 4 =$ 　　　　$24 \div 6 =$ 　　　　$36 \div 6 =$

$37 \div 8 =$ 　　　　$37 \div 9 =$ 　　　　$37 \div 10 =$

$37 \div 6 =$ 　　　　$54 \div 6 =$ 　　　　$54 \div 7 =$

Write the answer in the box.

$7 \overline{)45}$ 　　$8 \overline{)56}$ 　　$9 \overline{)43}$ 　　$6 \overline{)30}$ 　　$10 \overline{)35}$

$9 \overline{)12}$ 　　$5 \overline{)32}$ 　　$7 \overline{)44}$ 　　$7 \overline{)8}$ 　　$8 \overline{)34}$

$10 \overline{)53}$ 　　$9 \overline{)76}$ 　　$5 \overline{)54}$ 　　$7 \overline{)43}$ 　　$3 \overline{)27}$

$6 \overline{)42}$ 　　$7 \overline{)63}$ 　　$9 \overline{)42}$ 　　$8 \overline{)83}$ 　　$5 \overline{)49}$

Write the answer in the box.

$8 \div 6 =$ 　　　　$12 \div 10 =$ 　　　　$11 \div 9 =$

$13 \div 10 =$ 　　　　$17 \div 7 =$ 　　　　$23 \div 8 =$

$70 \div 10 =$ 　　　　$70 \div 7 =$ 　　　　$54 \div 6 =$

Choose the operation

Write either x or ÷ in the box.

6   ×   7 = 42   24   ÷   6 = 4   10   ÷   2 = 5

Write either x or ÷ in the box.

35 ☐ 7 = 5	35 ☐ 5 = 7	7 ☐ 5 = 35
5 ☐ 7 = 35	6 ☐ 9 = 54	54 ☐ 6 = 9
9 ☐ 6 = 54	54 ☐ 9 = 6	32 ☐ 4 = 8
4 ☐ 8 = 32	8 ☐ 4 = 32	32 ☐ 8 = 4
4 ☐ 9 = 36	36 ☐ 4 = 9	9 ☐ 4 = 36
36 ☐ 9 = 4	80 ☐ 8 = 10	8 ☐ 10 = 80
7 ☐ 9 = 63	63 ☐ 7 = 9	63 ☐ 9 = 7
9 ☐ 7 = 63	9 ☐ 9 = 81	81 ☐ 9 = 9
64 ☐ 8 = 8	8 ☐ 8 = 64	25 ☐ 5 = 5
5 ☐ 5 = 25	16 ☐ 4 = 4	4 ☐ 4 = 16
7 ☐ 7 = 49	49 ☐ 7 = 7	3 ☐ 3 = 9
9 ☐ 3 = 3	100 ☐ 10 = 10	10 ☐ 10 = 100
50 ☐ 10 = 5	5 ☐ 8 = 40	40 ☐ 4 = 10
20 ☐ 5 = 4	4 ☐ 10 = 40	36 ☐ 6 = 6
3 ☐ 7 = 21	21 ☐ 3 = 7	7 ☐ 4 = 28
14 ☐ 10 = 140	140 ☐ 2 = 70	70 ☐ 10 = 7
42 ☐ 6 = 7	7 ☐ 10 = 70	72 ☐ 8 = 9
50 ☐ 5 = 10	20 ☐ 4 = 5	3 ☐ 8 = 24

Real life problems

Write the answer in the box.

There are 8 ink cartridges in each packet.
How many cartridges will there
be in 6 packets?

$8 \times 6 = 48$

48 cartridges

Write the answer in the box.

Ian shares 50 oranges equally between 6
elephants and gives the remainder to
the giraffes. How many oranges do
the giraffes receive?

There are 9 children at a birthday party
and each child has 4 chocolate cakes.
How many chocolate cakes do the
children have altogether?

Ben has 60 building bricks and puts
them in piles of 7. How many piles of 7
can Ben make?

Katy has seven 10p coins, four 5p coins,
and two 2p coins. How much does she
have altogether?

The dog buries four bones in each hole.
The dog has 36 bones. How many holes
must the dog dig?

Perimeter

Write the perimeter of this shape in the answer box.

2 cm

8 cm

8 cm
+ 2 cm
+ 8 cm
+ 2 cm

20 cm

Write the perimeter of each shape in the answer box.

5 cm

1 cm

4 cm

3 cm

8 cm

4 cm

6 cm

6 cm

2 cm

7 cm

8 cm

5 cm

4 cm

10 cm

9 cm

9 cm

12 cm

5 cm

20 cm

5 cm

Area

Write the area of the shape in the answer box.

1 cm

7 cm

1 x 7 = 7

7 cm²

Write the area of each shape in the answer box.

Area

Write the area of this shape in the answer box.

3 cm

8 cm

$3 \times 8 = 24$

$24 \ cm^2$

Write the area of each shape in the answer box.

9 cm

4 cm

10 cm

3 cm

3 cm

12 cm

9 cm

6 cm

9 cm

7 cm

7 cm

8 cm

10 cm

20 cm

25 cm

4 cm

26

Problems using time

Write the answer in the box.

How many minutes until twelve o'clock?

90 minutes

Write the answer in the box.

What will be the time in half an hour?

What was the time ten minutes ago?

How many minutes until 9 o'clock?

The clock is 20 minutes fast. What is the real time?

Write the answer in the box.

What was the time half an hour ago?

How many minutes until 4 o'clock?

How long until a quarter to 4?

How many minutes since 2 o'clock?

Write the answer in the box.

Is it morning or afternoon?

How many minutes until 4.00 p.m.?

What time did the watch show half an hour before this?

How many hours until quarter past 8 in the evening?

Reading timetables

	Otterbourne	Compton	Badger Farm	Winchester
Redline Bus	8.00	8.05	8.15	8.25
Wincarry	8.05	No stop	8.12	8.20
Sean's taxi	8.30	8.35	8.45	8.55
Transtrax	8.07	No stop	No stop	8.15

The timetable shows the times it takes to travel using different transport companies between Otterbourne and Winchester.

Write the answer in the box.

How long does Redline take between Otterbourne and Winchester?

When does Wincarry arrive at Badger Farm?

Where does Transtrax not stop?

Where is Sean's taxi at 8.35?

Does Wincarry stop at Compton?

How long does Redline take to travel between Badger Farm and Winchester?

Which is the fastest trip between Otterbourne and Winchester?

Which service arrives at five minutes to nine?

How long does Sean's taxi take between Otterbourne and Badger Farm?

Where is Wincarry at twelve minutes past eight?

Mode and median

Write the mode and the median of this row in the boxes.

| 4 | 2 | 2 | 1 | 6 | 3 | 2 |

The mode is   2   The median is   2

Write the mode of each row in the box.

2	3	7	4	2	7	2	1	
7	4	1	4	8	5	3	4	
5	3	5	3	5	3	4	5	
7	5	9	7	2	4	8	6	
4	3	4	3	4	3	4	5	
0	4	2	7	3	8	2	9	
3	2	1	2	2	3	2	3	
8	3	6	3	8	2	8	4	

Write the median of each row in the box.

4	8	6	3	9	6	7	
5	9	2	6	9	1	4	
6	3	8	6	1	7	6	
3	8	6	7	5	9	4	
1	8	3	4	2	6	5	
9	5	8	6	4	7	9	
2	5	2	3	1	2	3	
6	3	7	4	5	8	6	

Nets of 3D shapes

For which 3D shape is this the net?

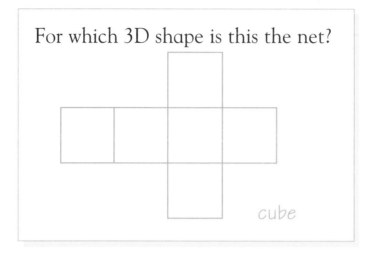

cube

For which 3D shapes are these the nets?

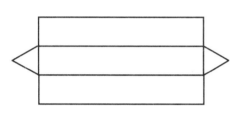

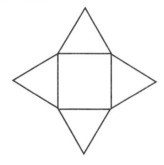

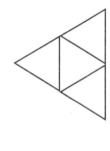

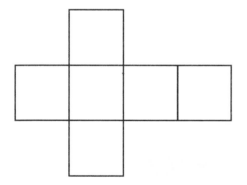

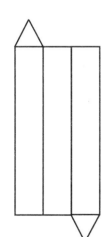

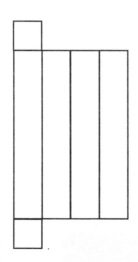

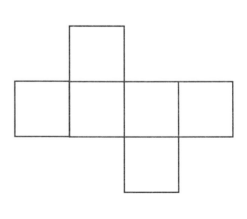

Nets of 3D shapes

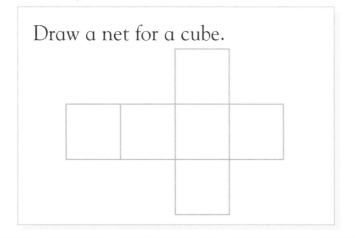

Draw a net for a cube.

Draw a net for these shapes.

Cuboid

Square-based pyramid

Cube (different to the example)

Triangular prism

Co-ordinates

Look at the grid and then answer the questions below.

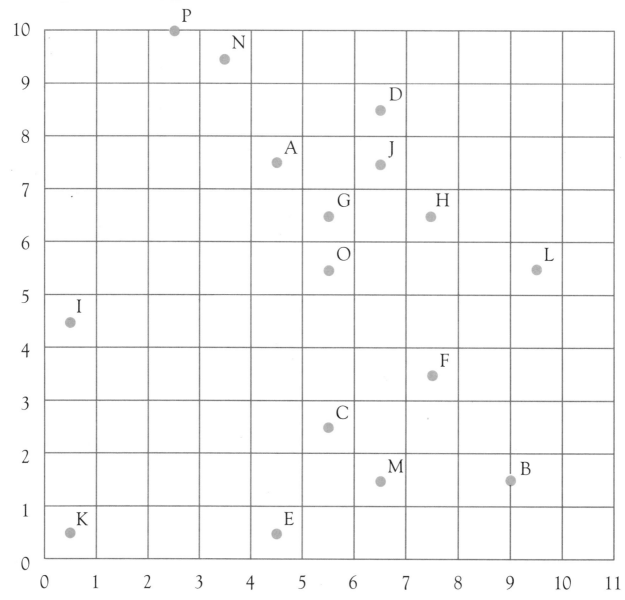

Give the co-ordinates of each letter.

A = $4\frac{1}{2}$, $7\frac{1}{2}$ B =   C =   D =

E =   F =   G =   H =

I =   J =   K =   L =

M =   N =   O =   P =